AIDA

Set in ancient Egypt, *Aida* is a story of love. In this special adaptation for young readers, prepared in cooperation with The Metropolitan Opera Guild, the Verdi opera has all the magic and beauty that have made it so famous throughout its years.

Aida is an Ethiopian slave girl at the court of the Pharaohs, who falls in love with Radames, an Egyptian warrior. Unknown to all, Aida is the daughter of the King of Ethiopia. Aida finds herself torn between her consuming love for Radames and her duty to her father. Leonard Everett Fisher's full-color double spreads display the dual pageantry of the ancient world and grand opera. And Florence Stevenson's text displays the romance and the intrigue of this much-loved opera.

A biographical note on the composer is included at the back of the book.

The Story of

AIDA

Based on the opera by Giuseppe Verdi

As retold by Florence Stevenson

Illustrations by Leonard Everett Fisher

In cooperation with The Metropolitan Opera Guild

G. P. Putnam's Sons   New York

AIDA

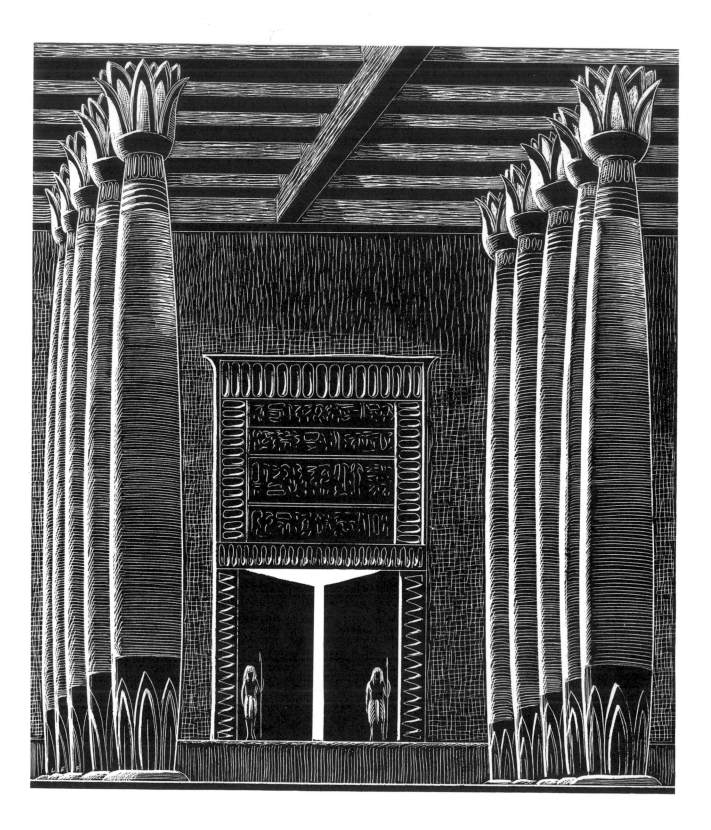

In the years behind these years, Memphis, where once had dwelt the Gods of Egypt, was greatest of all the cities that bordered the Nile. The finest houses, the tallest temples, the most magnificent statues of winged sphinxes and other beasts stretched along its sun-baked streets. It was in Memphis that the Pharaoh, mighty ruler of Egypt, held court.

The Pharaoh's palace was the most splendid in the world. It was made of many rare woods and had doors of bronze that caught the fire of sun. Its walls were bright with pictures of warriors and maidens and in it were hundreds of rooms. The loveliest of these were given to the Princess Amneris, only child of the Pharaoh. There, the floors were blue and painted with lotus buds, so that it seemed as if a vast lake rippled between the gilded pillars and the ivory couches.

The Princess lacked nothing. She wore rich garments and ate from golden dishes. Her every wish was granted by her fond father and if she was haughty and spoiled, he did not know it. He was so very proud of his pretty daughter that hardly a day passed without his bringing her a new treasure. Once it was a tame leopard on a silver chain and another time it was a full blown rose carved from a single ruby. He also gave her an Ethiopian slave girl of her own age, named Aida.

Although Aida was as dark as the princess was fair, she was even more beautiful, for, unlike her mistress, she had a kind and gentle nature. Unknown to the Pharaoh, Aida, too, was a Princess — daughter of his most powerful foe, Amonasro, the King of the Ethiopians. The Egyptians and the Ethiopians were always fighting each other, and it was in an Egyptian raid that the Ethiopian Princess had been captured.

Aida was very unhappy. She grieved for her dear father and she found Egypt's hot deserts very ugly after her own green jungles. It was also hard to be the slave of the Princess of Egypt, for Amneris was unkind to her. She made poor Aida run a thousand errands, carry heavy water jugs and serve at table.

Few pitied the little slave girl, but Aida had one friend — the handsome and noble Radames, Captain of the Palace guards. He loved her as much for her gentleness as for her beauty and vowed that one day he would take her to her own people.

But the great King of Ethiopia was already planning his daughter's rescue. Gathering his strongest warriors together, he invaded Egypt. The frightened people cried for help and in the temple of Ptah, Ramfis, the High Priest, prayed to the Goddess Isis for guidance. Appearing to him in a dream, Isis told him of a youth who would conquer the Ethiopians. Joyfully, Ramfis hurried off to inform the Pharaoh. As he entered the palace hall, he met Radames.

"Where are you going in such haste, Priest?" asked the youth.

"To the Pharaoh," replied Ramfis. "The Goddess Isis has this day given us the name of one who will lead Egypt to victory."

As Ramfis continued on his way, Radames sighed, "Oh, if only I could be that man. If I conquered the Ethiopians, I'd offer Aida a throne by my side."

"What are you thinking about, Radames?"

Radames turned to find the Princess Amneris standing behind him! He answered quickly, "I think of Egypt's peril, my lady."

"Oh?" said the Princess with a tiny pout. "I thought you might be dreaming of some fair maiden."

Amneris meant herself for she also loved the warrior and hoped that he had guessed her secret. But Radames, who disliked the Princess and feared her for Aida's sake, only frowned. His silence made Amneris suspicious. Did she have a rival?

As the Princess wondered, Aida entered quietly. A sudden smile brightened Radames' eyes and though he hastily looked down, Amneris had seen. Had Aida, her slave, won the heart of Radames? Her jealous anger nearly choked her, but she spoke gently: "My poor Aida, you seem disturbed. What troubles you?"

Aida was on her guard. "I — I fear for my country, Highness," she stammered, "for my people."

Amneris was sure that Aida had not told her the truth, but she could ask no more questions, for at this moment the Pharaoh and his court assembled in the hall. After a breathless messenger had brought the latest word of the invasion, the Pharaoh turned to face his court: "The Goddess Isis has given to us the name of Egypt's defender: *Radames!*"

The young soldier was overjoyed. He would have to leave at once, for Amonasro's men were storming the gates of Thebes. All, even Aida, hailed Radames, bidding him return victorious.

But when she was alone, Aida wept. If Radames triumphed, her people would be slain. Falling on her knees, the unhappy girl begged her Gods for help.

The priests escorted Radames to the temple of Ptah, and here Ramfis also called upon the Gods, asking protection for the soldier.

His prayers were answered, for after several anxious days word came that Radames had won a fierce battle. The desert sands were red with Ethiopian blood and many prisoners had been taken. Egypt was saved!

The Pharaoh ordered that a great procession be given in Thebes, the city Radames had rescued.

The hero would ride through the streets so that the Pharaoh and the people might honor him. The finest jewelers in the land set to making a golden wreath which Amneris herself would place on the warrior's head.

On the day of the ceremony, the slaves arrayed Amneris in a beautiful gown. They clasped a collar of gold and lapis around her neck and wound precious stones into her plaited black hair. Her copper mirror told her that she looked lovely, but she was not happy. She still wondered if Aida had dared to love Radames. As the girl entered, Amneris bade her women leave them together, for she had planned a cruel trick. Pretending to be sad, she said, "Oh, unhappy Egypt! Radames is dead!"

23

Aida's tears revealed her secret. Amneris' eyes darkened with anger. "I lied, slave. Radames lives!" At Aida's happy cry, the Princess' anger grew: "Know, slave, that I, daughter of the Pharaoh, love Radames!"

Aida dared not tell the Princess that she, too, was of royal birth, her equal. She forced herself to be humble and to beg for mercy. "You are rich and powerful, my lady. I have only love."

Amneris had no pity for Aida. She turned away from her, saying in harsh tones, "During the celebration, you shall sit at my feet. I will show you what it means to vie against me!"

All Thebes thronged the square as Amneris, resplendent in her golden cloak, mounted to a throne beside her father. Aida, who bore the Princess' train, arranged it in shining folds and knelt at her side. Banners waved and trumpets blew. "Glory to Egypt!" chanted the people.

"Glory to Egypt!" echoed the soldiers who marched in the streets and the priests who walked behind them. The priests carried poles on which were set images of Egypt's strange animal-headed gods: cats, birds, bulls, jackals. Some dancing girls turned somersaults and cartwheels, while others strewed rose petals before Radames' advancing chariot.

The hero drew rein before the royal throne. How handsome he looked in his burnished armor. As he dismounted, all the women blew him kisses, and as he knelt to receive the wreath, all the men shouted, "Glory to the conqueror!"

The Pharaoh rose to greet the noble youth. "Saviour of Egypt," he said, "ask what you will and you shall have it. By the Gods, I swear it!"

Radames longed to demand the hand of Aida, but he dared not voice his wish. Instead, he said, "Your Majesty must see the prisoners." At his signal, a mob of frightened men and women was driven into the square. Only one man walked proudly and fearlessly, a mighty warrior clad in a tiger skin. Aida, seeing him, shrieked and ran to him.

"Father!"

"Do not betray me," whispered the captive King. Then, turning to the Pharaoh, he said smoothly that he was, indeed,

Aida's father, a comrade of the fallen Amonasro. "Our King died in battle. If it was treason to fight for him," he added, "I, too, am ready to die."

Aida, however, joined the prisoners in begging for mercy. The people of Egypt added their voices to her plea. Only Ramfis the Priest, wary of Ethiopian trickery, demanded death. Radames stepped forward: "Mighty Pharaoh, hear my wish. I ask you to free the prisoners."

In spite of Ramfis' protests, the Pharaoh nodded. He had given his word. At the priest's insistence, he agreed to hold Aida's father hostage, but the others were unchained. The Pharaoh turned once more to Radames: "Generous Radames, you must have a reward. Take my daughter as bride. Some day you and she will rule Egypt."

Radames' heart was heavy, but he dared not refuse. He bowed before the Pharaoh. The triumphant Amneris looked scornfully at the weeping Aida, as she took Radames' outstretched hand.

Later that day, Radames sought Aida and made her promise to meet him at the Temple of Isis. This shrine was located some distance from the city gates and could be reached only by the river. As it was a spot visited by few, Aida and Radames had often come there.

Yet that night Amneris, led by Ramfis, also came to the temple to pray that Isis, Goddess of Love, smile on the Princess' marriage. By the time Aida arrived, the royal party had gone into the temple and the moon illuminated only the lonely shore and the dark river.

As Aida sorrowfully waited for Radames, Amonasro joined her. He bade her dry her tears and listen. His men were ready to fight again. If he knew of a road which remained unguarded, he could attack and overcome the Egyptians. Only Radames, as Commander, knew this secret.

"Radames loves you," hissed Amonasro. "You alone can win the secret from him."

Aida was shocked and frightened by her father's demands; she could not betray Radames! Her protests sent Amonasro into a fury.

"You are no daughter of mine," he cried. "You have become an Egyptian slave!"

The dark princess trembled beneath her father's wrath, for his words reminded her of her duty to Ethiopia and her royal blood. "Oh my country," she wept, "what sorrow you have cost me." Sadly, she agreed to obey. And none too soon, for Amonasro's sharp ears had caught the sound of Radames' footsteps on the path. With a final warning to Aida, Amonasro slipped into the bushes to listen.

Aida played her part well. When Radames spoke of his love for her, she scornfully reminded him that he was to wed Amneris. "If you wish to prove your love for me," she said, "you will leave this dry and burning land. You will flee with me — to my country."

"Leave — leave Egypt!" Radames could not bear the thought. But Aida insisted, "Only there can we be happy — only there can we be free."

At last Radames' love for Aida overcame even his love of country. He agreed to accompany her to Ethiopia and, having made that decision, was prepared to leave at once. But Aida hung back: "Are not all the roads guarded by your soldiers?"

Radames answered quickly, "Not the gorges of Napata."

"The gorges of Napata!" Amonasro sprang from his hiding place. "Then that is where I and my army will attack."

"You!" cried Radames, frozen with horror. "You are the King of Ethiopia!"

"Yes, I, Amonasro!"

"My country — I have betrayed my country," gasped Radames.

"Take heart," said wily Amonasro. "You and Aida will be happy in our land. Come with us!" But as he seized the soldier's hand, an angry voice rang out: *"Traitor!"*

Amneris and Ramfis had come out of the temple in time to hear the plotter. "Traitor!" repeated the Princess. Amonasro, dagger in hand, leaped at her, but Radames ran between them. "Go!" he warned. Amonasro, dragging Aida, dashed out, the guard in hot pursuit.

Radames made no attempt to escape.

Unsheathing his sword, he handed it to Ramfis: "Priest, I am your prisoner."

All Egypt was shocked at Radames' treason. The youth was locked in a palace dungeon, but as the hour of his trial drew near, Amneris' conscience gave her no peace. In her heart, she knew Radames was not a traitor. An appeal to her father could save him. Yet, *he* would only return to Aida — Aida who, unlike Amonasro, had escaped the swords of the guards.

Swallowing her pride, Amneris ordered Radames to be brought before her. She begged him to forget Aida and rule with her in Egypt, but Radames refused. He wanted nothing of the wicked Amneris. Angrily, the jealous Princess allowed the priests to take Radames before their dread tribunal.

But when he had gone, the Princess fell to her knees on the stone floor. Her fury was soon vanquished by her fear, as from the underground judgment chamber rose the accusing voices of the priestly tribunal. Three times she heard stern Ramfis hurl the charge of treason at Radames and three times she shuddered as the youth failed to reply. In vain the anguished princess waited for him to defend himself. He remained silent, even while the priests chanted "traitor." As their cries rang through the halls, she begged the Gods of Egypt to save the soldier. But the Gods were silent.

Radames was judged guilty and condemned to be buried alive.

In vain Amneris protested the terrible punishment. "Cruel Ramfis," she hissed, "you want revenge on him!" The priest ignored her tears and curses. "Radames must die," he said.

No cheering crowds followed Radames to the temple of Ptah that night. No one but the priests saw him descend the steps into a vault that gaped open in the temple floor. As he reached the bottom, a marble slab was fitted into the opening, shutting out light and air. Radames' spirits did not fail. He sat quietly in the darkness, awaiting death. His only thoughts were for Aida. "Oh, Aida," he sighed, "I shall never see you again."

Suddenly, two soft arms slipped around his neck and a face pressed against his. "Radames!" Aida had been waiting in the vault, to share his fate.

"Aida!" mourned Radames, "you must not die. You are too young, too lovely!"

"Hush, beloved," whispered the girl. "We will be together in heaven."

Above them the priests chanted and clouds of incense curled about the image of Ptah. The Princess Amneris, clad in black, came in and threw herself upon the slab that sealed the tomb of Radames. Tearfully, she prayed that the Gods forgive her sin and grant eternal rest to the hero.

Even as Amneris wept, the Gods proved kind, for death had come quickly to Aida, and Radames soon followed her into the realm of shadows.

GIUSEPPE VERDI AND *Aida*

Giuseppe Verdi, Italy's greatest operatic composer (1813-1901), was born in Le Roncole, a tiny village in northern Italy. Verdi's parents were humble people. But when they learned that their son had a genius for music and composition, they encouraged the lad. They bought him an old spinet and saw that he had lessons. Later, a local merchant from a nearby town helped young Verdi to go to the city of Milan and apply to the Conservatory. By some mischance, Verdi's application was refused and he was forced to study privately.

Verdi's first success came in 1842 with *Nabucco*, an opera based on the life of Nebuchadnezzar, the Babylonian king. In the following years, he wrote such works as *Macbeth*, *Il Trovatore*, *Rigoletto*, *La Traviata*, *La Forza del Destino*, and many others.

Aida, Verdi's twenty-fifth opera, was commissioned by the Khedive of Egypt to celebrate the opening of the Suez Canal, which linked the Mediterranean with the Red Sea. The canal was completed in 1869; three years later on Christmas Eve, 1871, the world premiere of *Aida* took place at the Cairo Opera House. Although Antonio Ghislanzoni, Verdi's countryman, is credited with the libretto, and the French writer Mariette Bey wrote the original story, much of the exciting action in the opera was supplied by Verdi himself. *Aida*, instantly successful, still ranks as one of the world's most popular operas.

About Florence Stevenson

FLORENCE STEVENSON is currently a Contributing Editor to *Opera News* and also writes for the Metropolitan Opera and Philharmonic Hall programs. She is an Associate Editor of *FM Magazine* and has written for *Show* and *Theatre Arts*. A graduate of the University of Southern California, the author won the Theatre Americana first prize for an original play. Miss Stevenson now lives in the heart of New York City.

About Leonard Everett Fisher

LEONARD EVERETT FISHER, a painter, author and former dean of a professional art school, is the illustrator of close to 100 books for young people. A native New Yorker, he was awarded the Pulitzer Prize for Art in 1950. His most recent book for Putnam's, *Ride the Cold Wind*, was included on the American Library Association's list of notable children's books. Mr. Fisher, his wife and three children live in Westport, Connecticut.